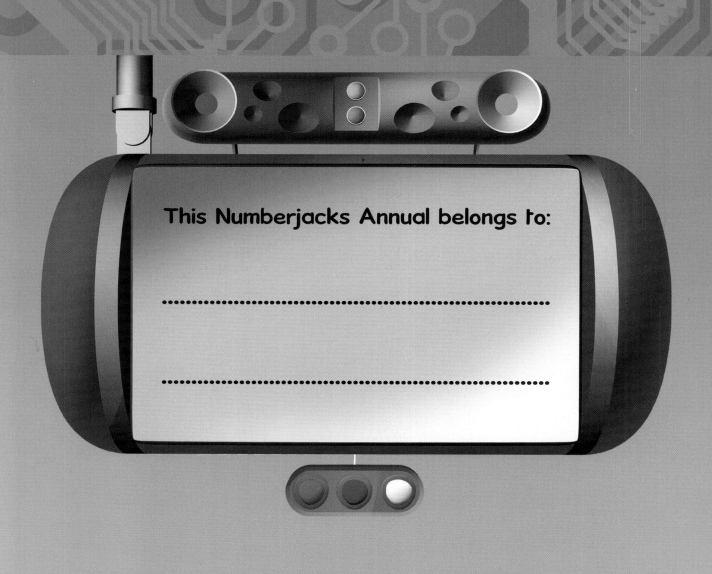

This Numberjacks Annual belongs to:

....

....

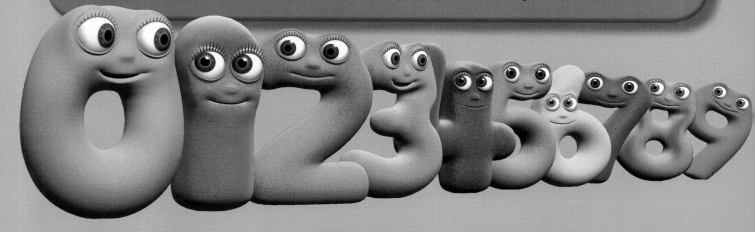

Hello!

We're the Numberjacks and this is our special annual!
Inside, you can read about our secret missions and adventures
with the Meanies. There are lots of pictures for you to
look at. You can help us solve puzzles and problems, too.

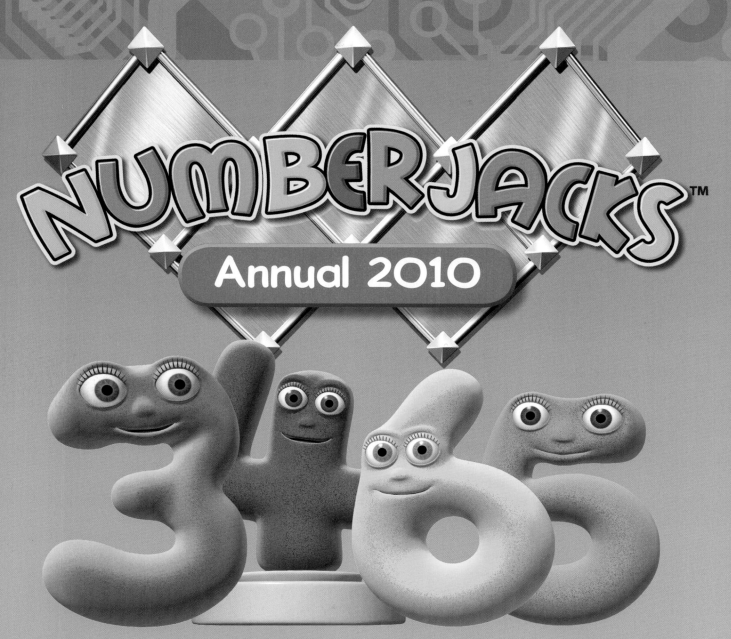

NUMBERJACKS™

Annual 2010

EGMONT

We bring stories to life

First published in Great Britain in 2009 by Egmont UK Limited
239 Kensington High Street, London W8 6SA

Numberjacks™ & © 2009 Open Mind Productions Ltd.
Licensed by Granada Ventures Ltd.

Editor: Nina Filipek
Designer: Paul Dronsfield

ISBN 978 1 4052 4639 2
1 3 5 7 9 10 8 6 4 2
Printed in Italy

An Open Mind Production

GRANADA Ventures

Note to parents: adult supervision is recommended when sharp-pointed items such as scissors are in use.

Contents

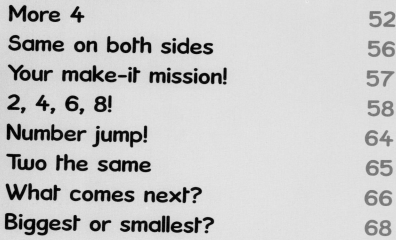

Look out for us!

Look out for us as you read the annual. Write the page number or tick the box the first time you see us.

This is a Meanie-Watch Area.

I'm watching you! Ha, ha, ha!

Know your Numberjacks!

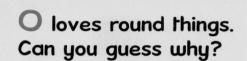

O loves round things. Can you guess why?

Bloob!

Oooh!

1 is a small number. But look what happens when 1 and O stand together! What number do they make? Find ten hidden footballs on these pages.

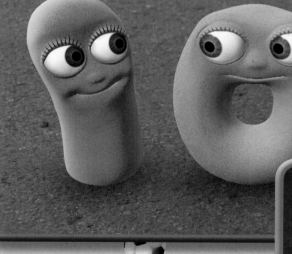

2 is counting and jumping in the Brain Gain Machine! Try counting and jumping at the same time!

One, two!

8's buddy blocks are hiding on these pages. Help the Numberjacks to find them all. Here's one of them.

Coming ready or not, buddy blocks!

9 checks that all the Numberjacks are safely back home. Is everyone here? Say their numbers in order.

Stand still, while I check we're all here!

In an Ordinary Sofa!

In an Ordinary Sofa, extraordinary things are happening!
Take a look inside!

1 Control Room

This is where the
Numberjacks take calls
from the Agents in
the outside world.
The Numberjacks can
talk to the Agents and
see what's happening
on big screens.

2 Gym

The Numberjacks love to keep
fit and the Gym is one of their
favourite places. Here, they
can practise their best jumping.
Who is jumping in the Gym?

③ Brain Gain Machine

The Brain Gain Machine makes Brain Gain. This is the powerful joined-up thinking that the Numberjacks use to solve problems. Who can you see inside the machine?

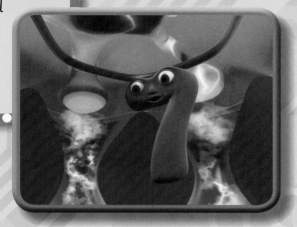

④ Launcher

The Numberjacks have their own special launch pods inside the Launcher. This machine flings them out of the sofa in hundreds of tiny pieces. Which Numberjack is flying out of the sofa?

⑤ Cosy Room

The Cosy Room is where the Numberjacks like to relax. Sometimes they play with the Beautiful Things and sometimes they read books. Who can you see in the Cosy Room?

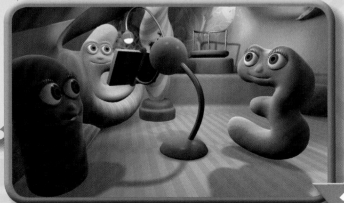

Meet the Meanies!

If you haven't met the **Meanies** before, look out because they love making mischief!

Oh, no! 5 is seeing double trouble! The **Puzzler** has made two of himself! Make both Puzzlers go away by solving his puzzle.

"You have two plants and then two more. How many is that – three or four?"

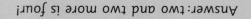

Answer: two and two more is four!

The **Numbertaker** likes to take numbers away. He uses all kinds of grabbers and sucker-uppers that he hides up his sleeves.

Here are three balloons. If the Numbertaker pops two, how many will be left?

Answer: one balloon.

It's the **Problem Blob!** His blobs of bright green slime cause big problems.

How many blobs of slime are coming from the Problem Blob?

The **Shape Japer** is up to her tricks again!
She's changed the shape of these peas into cubes!

What shape is the Shape Japer?

Answer: the Shape Japer is a cube. Her face is a square.

16

Spooky Spoon is stirring up more trouble.

What has she done now?

She's swapped the children's
clothes for grown-ups' clothes!

17

Spot the difference

The Numberjacks have been playing with the Beautiful Things. Look at the pictures carefully. Find six differences in picture 2. Circle the differences and tick the box as you find each one.

I have found this many differences:

1	2	3	4	5	6
☐	☐	☐	☐	☐	☐

Answers: a Beautiful Thing has appeared inside the box and the wheel is missing. Numberjack 1 and two stars have appeared. The pink cube is smaller.

Just think!

The Numberjacks know that **powerful thinking** is the way to solve problems. Use your powerful thinking (that's your very own Brain Gain!) to solve these puzzles and problems.

The Numbertaker has taken some candles from this cake.
How many more candles do you need to make five altogether?
Draw the missing candles.

The handle on the cleaner's mop is too long!
Which Meanie could have done this?

Spooky Spoon has mixed up the Numberjacks' colours. Colour them in and put them right again!

Now she's mixed up the door numbers! Which number comes first?

8 or 9

4 or 6

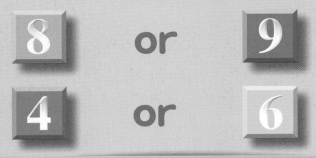

Remember, next time you have a puzzle or a problem to solve, use Brain Gain!

Bad circles!

One day the alarm rang. It was Agent 16. "Things are going wrong!" she told the Numberjacks.

4 soon put the problem on the screen. A boy's Frisbee was stuck in his hand. The Frisbee was trying to **throw the boy**!

Next, a girl's plate was being very silly. It wouldn't keep still. Her jelly was **wibble-wobbling** all over the place!

Bet you can't wibble-wobble like a jelly!

"We're on our way," 6 told the Agent. "I think this is one for me!"

Count down with the Numberjacks to launch 6.

6 5 4 3 2 1 0

23

What things are the same about the Frisbee and the plate?

Agent 16 had an answer. "I think it's their **shape**! They are both circles!" she said.

Who do **you** think was causing the problems?

It was the **Shape Japer**! She laughed when the cleaner's bucket poured water all over him and when the gardener's flowerpot went potty!

What is the same about the bucket and the flowerpot?

Circles were **going bad** everywhere!
"We've got to do something or else anything can happen," said 5.

Why might the wheels fall off the cars?

5 was right to be worried. Soon there were more problems for the Numberjacks.

The bat had a circular hole in it.

The cup had a hole in it, too!

3 powered up the Brain Gain Machine. "Give the **Shape Japer** so many circles to worry about that she won't be able to handle it!" suggested Agent 16.

"**Make circles, make circles!**" said 3, bouncing up and down.

6 took a zap of powerful Brain Gain.

You've been zapped, too!
Use the Brain Gain to help you think of a way of making a circle.
Could you make a circle with your hands or your mouth? Or with play clay? Or in any other way?

The girl made circles in the sand with her cup.
The gardener made a circle with a hosepipe.

The Shape Japer bounced from circle to circle, getting bigger in big circles and smaller in small circles. Finally, she disappeared inside one of the circles!

"Aaaah!" she cried.

"Did the trick!" said 6, proudly.

That was the end of another successful mission for the Numberjacks!

Use Brain Gain!
Look around where you are.
Can you see any little circles or
big circles?
Draw one of the circles you can see here.

27

Circles, circles everywhere!

Draw

Draw a circle going all the way round and back to the beginning.

Draw a circle going **around** Shape Japer. Then draw a circle **inside** 6!

Draw around these circles.

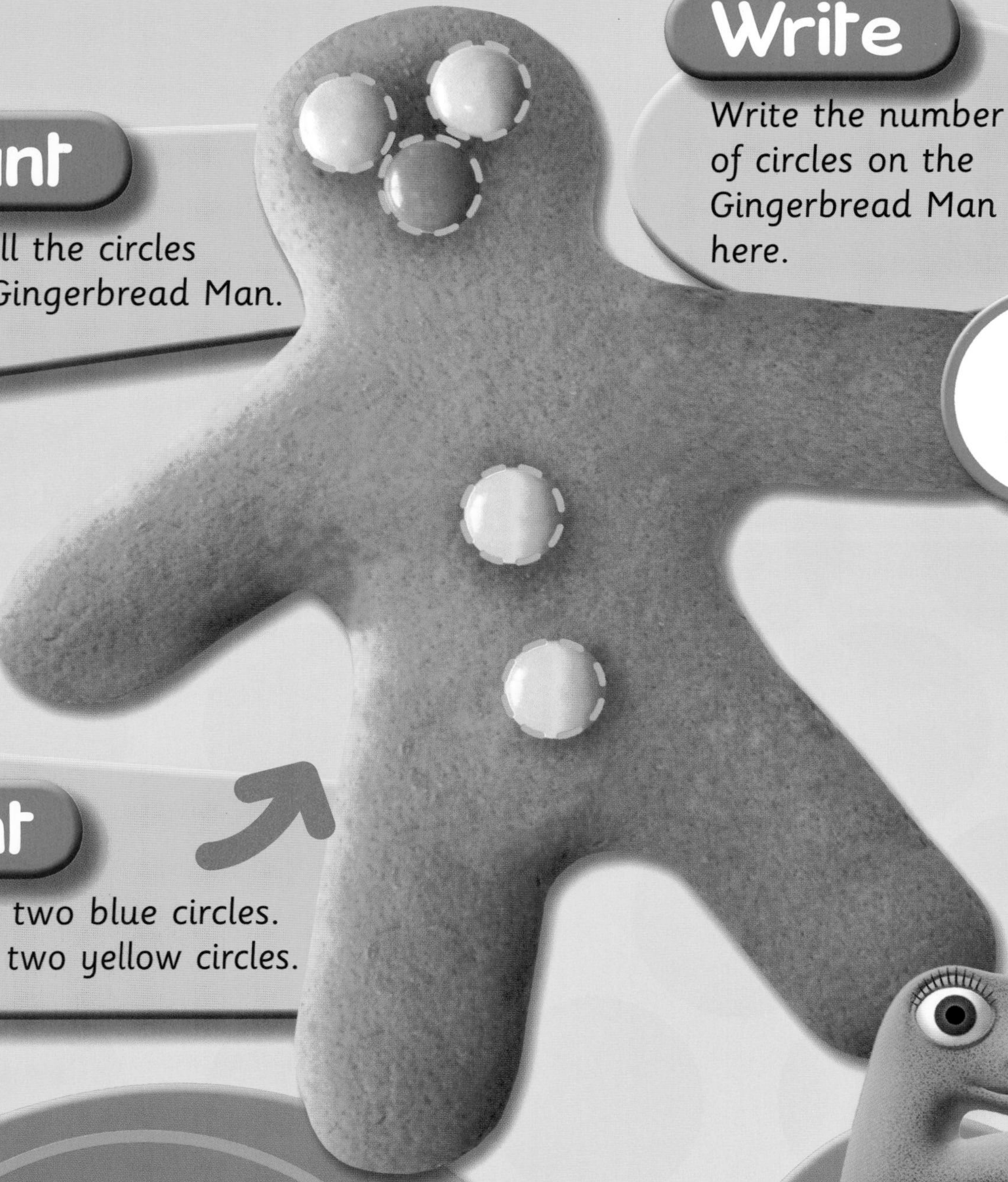

Count

Count all the circles on the Gingerbread Man.

Write

Write the number of circles on the Gingerbread Man here.

5

Point

Point to two blue circles.
Point to two yellow circles.

Look

Look for **little** circles inside **bigger** circles. Follow a circle with your finger.

29

Shape race

You will need a counter for each player, a dice and a friend to play this game with.

1 START

2 Wave two hands.

Go forward 3 shapes.

Go forward to a triangle.

20 FINISH

19 Laugh like the Puzzler and go back 1 shape.

18

Go forward 1 shape.

16

15 Make 'blobby' noises and go back 2 shapes.

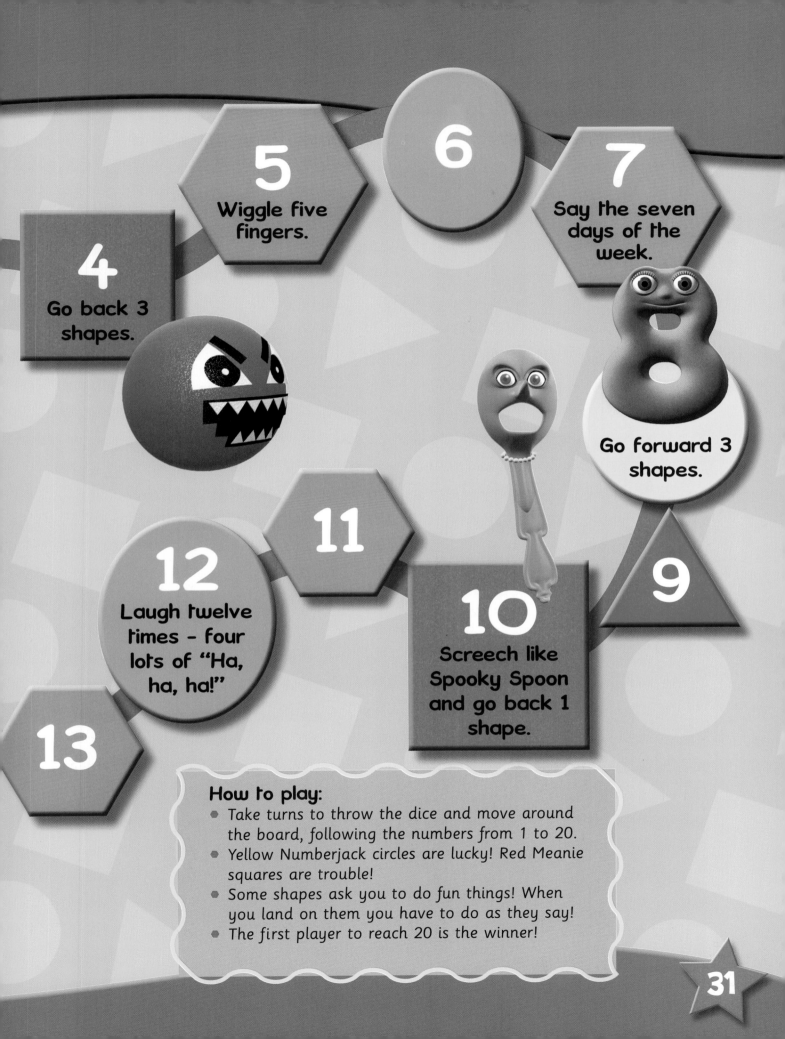

4 Go back 3 shapes.

5 Wiggle five fingers.

6

7 Say the seven days of the week.

8 Go forward 3 shapes.

9

10 Screech like Spooky Spoon and go back 1 shape.

11

12 Laugh twelve times – four lots of "Ha, ha, ha!"

13

How to play:
- Take turns to throw the dice and move around the board, following the numbers from 1 to 20.
- Yellow Numberjack circles are lucky! Red Meanie squares are trouble!
- Some shapes ask you to do fun things! When you land on them you have to do as they say!
- The first player to reach 20 is the winner!

31

Fit the shape

Look

The Shape Japer changed her shape so that she fitted inside a round bucket.

Numberjack 1 fits inside this rocket shape!

Think

How many squares will 3 need to finish this doorway?

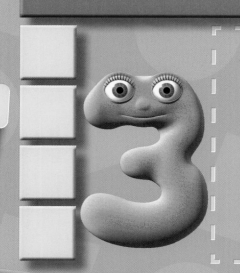

Answer: four squares.

Look

Sometimes the Shape Japer can be a pointy shape. How many pointy corners does the edge of her face have when she's a triangle?

Count

Look for pointy corners at this picnic. How many pointy corners are there **altogether**?

Draw

Draw one line to cut this square into **two triangles**.

Use Brain Gain! Make a triangle shape with the corner of the page.

Favourite toys

The Numberjacks would like to share their favourite games with you.

Thinkyjump Machine

This is a game where you have to think and jump. Jump your finger on things that are the same colour. Now jump on things that are the same shape.

Bloop Ball

The Bloop Ball is green, big and 'bloopy'! It can hang in the air! Find the Bloop Ball that's hiding on these pages.

Seesaw

The Numberjacks like to play balancing games on the seesaw. Which end has the most buddy blocks? Which end is the heaviest? Which end is the lightest? How do you know?

Beeper

The Beeper can be lots of fun because it works like a clock and can measure how long it takes the Numberjacks to do things. Read the number on the Beeper. Count to seven and say something that you think you could do in this amount of time!

7

Dice

The Numberjacks like to play games with the big Hover Dice. Ask an adult to trace over this shape and make a cube. Then draw the dots on to make a dice. The dots on opposite sides add up to seven.

fold

- - - - -

cut

_____

Use Brain Gain!
Draw shapes on the dice instead of dots. Roll the dice, then find something that matches the shape.

35

Estimate

Estimate is a game where you have to guess at how many things there are – without counting them. Try it!

Which of 3's boxes contains **five** of her Beautiful Things? Draw a circle around the one you think it is.

Try to do this without counting!

How many rings are there? Make a guess and tick the box.

less than 4 ☐

more than 4 ☐

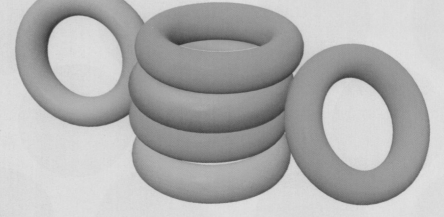

See if you can answer these without counting.

Do you think there are enough sandwiches for **seven** people to have one each?

yes ☐ no ☐

If **nine** people came to your party do you think there are enough sandwiches here for one each?

yes ☐ no ☐

Estimate the number of Dancing Cows!
Is it nearer **ten** or nearer **twenty**?
Tick the box.

nearer 10 ☐

nearer 20 ☐

Who's missing?

Say who's missing from this page. The buddy blocks are your clues!

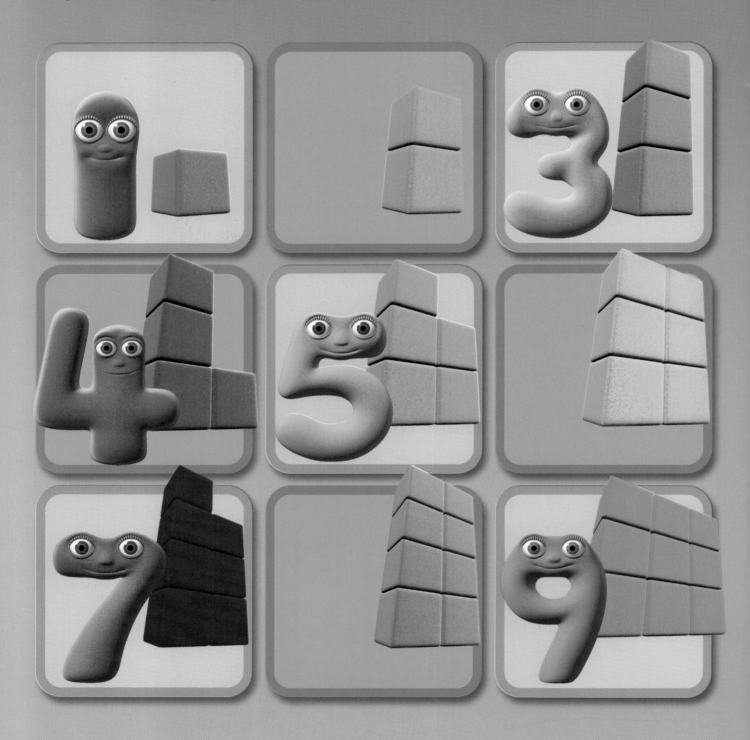

38

The Puzzler's maze

The Puzzler has set **you** a puzzle! Follow the Numberjacks in order from 0 to 9 to find your way through the Puzzler's maze.

Start

Finish

39

Time trouble

You can help read this story. When you see the pictures of the characters, say their names.

Three   **Four**   **Five**   **Six**   **Spooky Spoon**

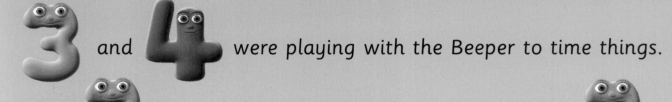

3 and 4 were playing with the Beeper to time things.

Could 3 keep **quiet** for ten beeps? **No way!** Could 3 be

noisy for 10 beeps? **Probably!**

> Well, there we are! Argle bargle boo! I love making noise, don't you?

40

was timing being noisy when the alarm rang.

The Numberjacks could see a man in a cafe whose food had been taken

away from him before he had time to eat it! "We're on our way!"

said , as jumped into the Launcher.

Straightaway, saw what the problem was. It was  !

Why is the man in the cafe unhappy?

Who is causing the problem?

41

"I'm making sure nobody has got enough time to do anything!"

laughed . "We've got to stop  !" said  .

 started up the Brain Gain Machine. "Give them more time!"

shouted , bouncing up and down inside. **Bzzz! Zap!**

Oh, no! Now people were taking too much time! In the cafe, the

food went cold because the waitress took too long to serve it!

Then had an idea. "We can use my Beeper!"

Now the Numberjacks could give things the right amount of

time and everything would be back to normal.

What colour is the Beeper?

43

"We can time anything, , and stop you messing it up!" said . "I'll get you!" said . She chased into the playground.

We can time anything!

I'll get you!

Again, jumped into the Brain Gain Machine. **Bzzz! Bzzz! Zap!**

"Set the beeper to zero beeps!" cried  .

Time had run out for 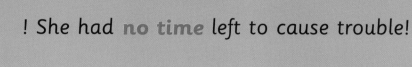 ! She had no time left to cause trouble!

Can you guess what happened next?

 vanished into thin air! Hurray for the Numberjacks!

Water clock!

You can find out how long it takes you to do different things by using a water clock!

You will need: a paper cup, a washing-up bowl, water.

1 Ask an adult to make a little hole in the bottom of a paper cup.

2 Hold your finger over the hole and fill to the top with water.

3 Hold the cup over a washing-up bowl and move your finger away from the hole.

4 Find out what you can do before the cup empties.
For example: can you say your favourite nursery rhyme?
What else can you do?

Time to go!

Hickory, dickory, dock!
I made a water clock.
The clock went drip,
I took a sip,
Hickory, dickory, dock!

Just in time!

Count

Numberjack 5 knows another way of counting time.

Say out loud:
1 Numberjack, 2 Numberjack, 3 Numberjack, 4 Numberjack . . . and so on.

The time it takes you to say, "1 Numberjack" is about as long as **one second**. So now you can time your friends doing different things!

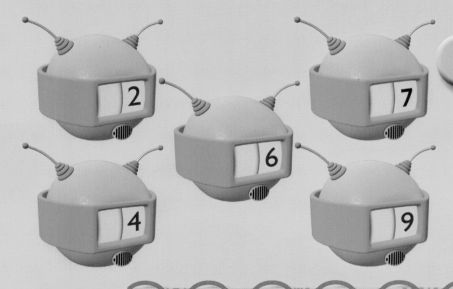

Say

Say the numbers on the Beepers in order from the **shortest** to the **longest** time.

Look

Which number is missing on the clock?

Answers: 2, 4, 6, 7, 9; number 6 is missing.

What if . . .

What if a glove had fifteen fingers?

Would it better than a glove with five fingers?

What if a racing car had fourteen wheels?

Would it go faster or slower than one with four wheels?

What if there was more than one sun in the sky?

Would you feel hotter or colder?

What if a flower had only one petal?

Would it be smellier or not as smelly as one with lots of petals?

Think up some "what if" ideas of your own.

49

The worst moment for the Numberjacks was when half of a girl's birthday cake went missing. Who do you think was to blame?

The best moment was when the Numberjacks split the Shape Japer into two halves. They really taught her a lesson that time!

Another bad moment was when the Numbertaker was taking groups of more than one. 5 was worried about what might happen to these three children.

It was a great moment when 1 grew bigger and bigger. Soon, 1 was so big that even the Numbertaker was scared! Look at how big 1 is compared to 6.

It was a scary moment when something went wrong with the Launcher. One by one the Numberjacks disappeared from the sofa and found themselves outside.

First to go was 1.
Second was 2.
Third was 3.

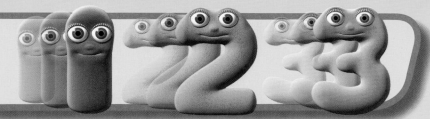

And so it carried on until all the Numberjacks were stuck outside – all except little 0!

But clever little 0 got in the Brain Gain Machine and brought all the Numberjacks home by counting back from nine to zero!

Help O to count down.

9 → 8 → 7 → 6 → 5 → 4 → 3 → 2 → 1 → 0

1

The Numberjacks were having problems! Lots of things were changing shape on one side. The builder's plank of wood had grown an extra bit on one end. He wanted both ends to be the same.

2

"Sides that should match don't any more!" said Agent 38. So 4 headed off to sort out the problem. "It's the Shape Japer!" cried 4. "We must make both sides match again!" Agent 38 said.

3

But things got worse when the Shape Japer started changing people! A man had an extra arm! Then an extra leg! Now the two sides of his body didn't match.

4

The man was very worried and 5 was worried, too. If a butterfly had wings that didn't match, it wouldn't be able to fly properly.

5

The Numberjacks wanted to make everything match again. 8 agreed to help. Why could 8 help? Both sides of Numberjack 8 matched. Colour in 8 so that both sides match in colour as well as shape.

6

8 jumped inside the Brain Gain Machine. It bubbled and buzzed with lots of joined-up thinking. But 8 made too much Brain Gain and it was too strong!

7

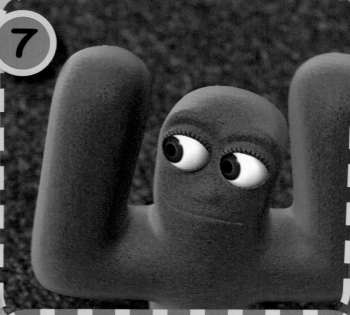

Look what's happened to 4! Now 4's sides looked the same! The Shape Japer couldn't stop laughing.

8

"Can I help?" said 7. "My sides are completely different." Then 7 and 8 both jumped inside the Brain Gain Machine. The Numberjacks sent the Shape Japer both kinds of Brain Gain.

9

At first the Shape Japer's sides matched, then they didn't match, then they matched again. She kept on changing shape until, at last, she gave up!

10

Now 4 was back to normal again. "Thanks," said 4. "It was weird having matching sides."

11

Everything else went back to normal, too. The man was very pleased to have matching sides!

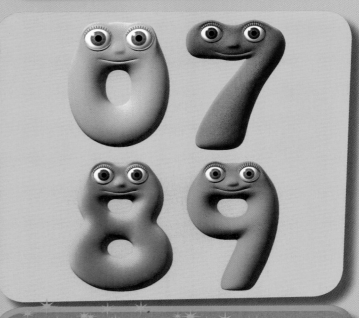

Use Brain Gain!
Which of these Numberjacks have sides that don't match?

Same on both sides

You can make the Shape Japer cross by making these things the same on both sides!

Colour the butterfly so that it is the same on both sides.

Finish drawing the face so that it is the same on both sides.

Bet you can't finish O!

Your make-it mission!

You will need: a sheet of plain paper, a pencil, scissors, paints, paintbrushes.

1. Fold the sheet of paper in half. Then open it out.

2. Paint some thick blobs on one half.

3. Fold over the other half. Press down. Then open out again. Leave to dry.

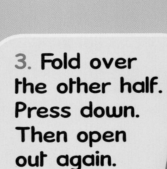

4. Fold the paper over. Draw and carefully cut out half of a butterfly shape. Ask an adult to help you do this!

5. Open out for a super surprise!

2, 4, 6, 8!

One day three boys were playing a board game when some numbers disappeared from the dice! They had only one, three and five left!

Which numbers are missing?

"Two, four and six are missing!" said 6.
The Numberjacks agreed that 6 should go on the mission.

Where has 6 landed – on a door or a wall?

Then Agent 57 called in to tell the Numberjacks about a problem with a mobile phone. 6 could see that some of the numbers were missing.

Look carefully at the phone. Which numbers are missing?

"Two, four, six and eight are missing!" said 6.

"Why those numbers?" 5 wondered.

Agent 57 knew the answer. "They are the numbers you get if you count in twos!"

Can you guess who has made these numbers go missing?

"I've spotted the Numbertaker!" cried 6.
The Numbertaker was taking house numbers!

"He's got a two! What will be next?" said 3.
If the Numbertaker was counting in twos, 4 knew which number would be next — it was going to be a four!

What number will be next after four?

Yes, it's two, four, then six!
6 was lucky to escape! "He's moving on!" cried 6. "I think I'm going to need help!"
"I'll send for number 8!" said 4.

5 thought about what might happen if the Numbertaker wasn't stopped . . .

He wouldn't let you be four years old. You'd go straight from being three to being five! Imagine that!

Numberjack 8 went outside to help. Then 2 and 4 jumped into the Brain Gain Machine.

They were going to jump and count in twos.

You can jump and count in twos with them!

The Numbertaker was just about to suck up Numberjack 6 when 8 shouted, "Numbertaker, this way!"

The Numbertaker turned towards 8, then towards 6. He couldn't decide: 6 or 8? Then he spun round and round in confusion – and disappeared!

Hooray! They'd done it!

At last, the dice had got its numbers back and the boys could finish their game!

Now the Numberjacks played a game of their own.

"2, 4, 6, 8 . . .
We're the numbers who
are great!"

"1 and 3, 5, 7 and 9 . . .
We're the numbers who
are fine!"

Use Brain Gain!
Who do you think they had forgotten?

63

Number jump!

Here's how to play Number jump! All you need is a counter.

1	
2	
3	
4	
5	
6	
7	
8	
9	

Put your counter on number 1 and show Numberjack 1 how to jump along the number track in ones. Say the names of the numbers you land on.

Now put your counter on number 2 and show Numberjack 2 how to jump along the number track in twos.

Two the same

Find two things that look exactly the same in each group. Match them with a line each time. Are there any things that are nearly the same?

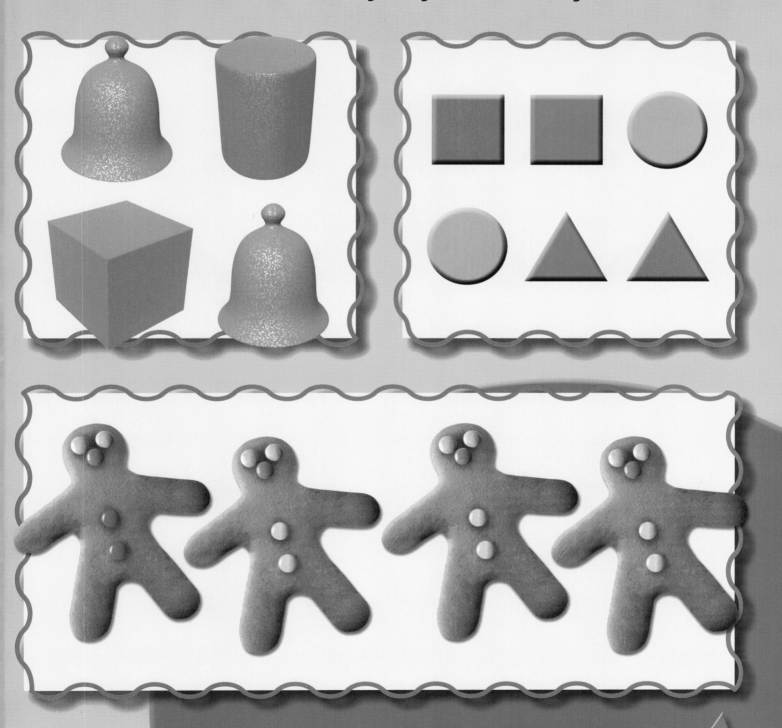

What comes next?

Say

Say or draw what comes next in each row on the Diamond Screens.

Draw

Help 3 to make a pattern with the Beautiful Things by drawing what comes next.

Try to make a pattern with your own toys.

Jump

6 is making a pattern, too.
6 is doing: a jump, a jump
then a turn! Jump, jump, turn!

See if you can make up your own
jumping pattern.

Try hop, hop,
jump, jump!

Look

Someone's made a pattern with these bottles!
Work out what the pattern is.

Use Brain Gain!
Look for patterns
around you.

Answers: an orange, Numberjack 8, two red circles, a purple cone,
two green bottles then two blue bottles.

Biggest or smallest?

A game for two to four players.

How to play:

- Take turns to close your eyes and point to a number on this page.
- The winner is the player who points to the biggest number.
- If you point in between two numbers then take the bigger number as your score.
- In the next round, the winner is the player who points to the smallest number!

Look out for the fantastic Numberjacks Magazine!

Available at all good supermarkets and newsagents

On sale every 3 weeks!

2 FREE GIFTS!

75 stickers inside

Issue 13

Counting ✓
Thinking ✓
Doing ✓

Long! Short!

Measuring in the zoo!

We're measuring!

How tall are you?

Based on the AWARD WINNING hit TV programme!*

Fantastic free gift with every issue!

✓ Builds your child's **CONFIDENCE** with numbers!

✓ features loads of **ACTIVITIES** — children have fun and learn at the same time!

✓ Supports Early Years **FOUNDATION STAGE** and beyond!

To learn about the Numberjacks, and for more fun and games, visit
www.numberjacks.co.uk